THE PARK IS OPEN

WWW.JURASSICPARK.COM

JURASSIC WORLD: THE PARK IS OPEN
A CENTUM BOOK 9781910114810
Published in Great Britain by Centum Books Ltd

This edition published 2015

A CIP catalogue record for this book is available from the British Library

Printed in Italy
1 3 5 7 9 10 8 6 4 2

WELCOME TO
JURASSIC WOR

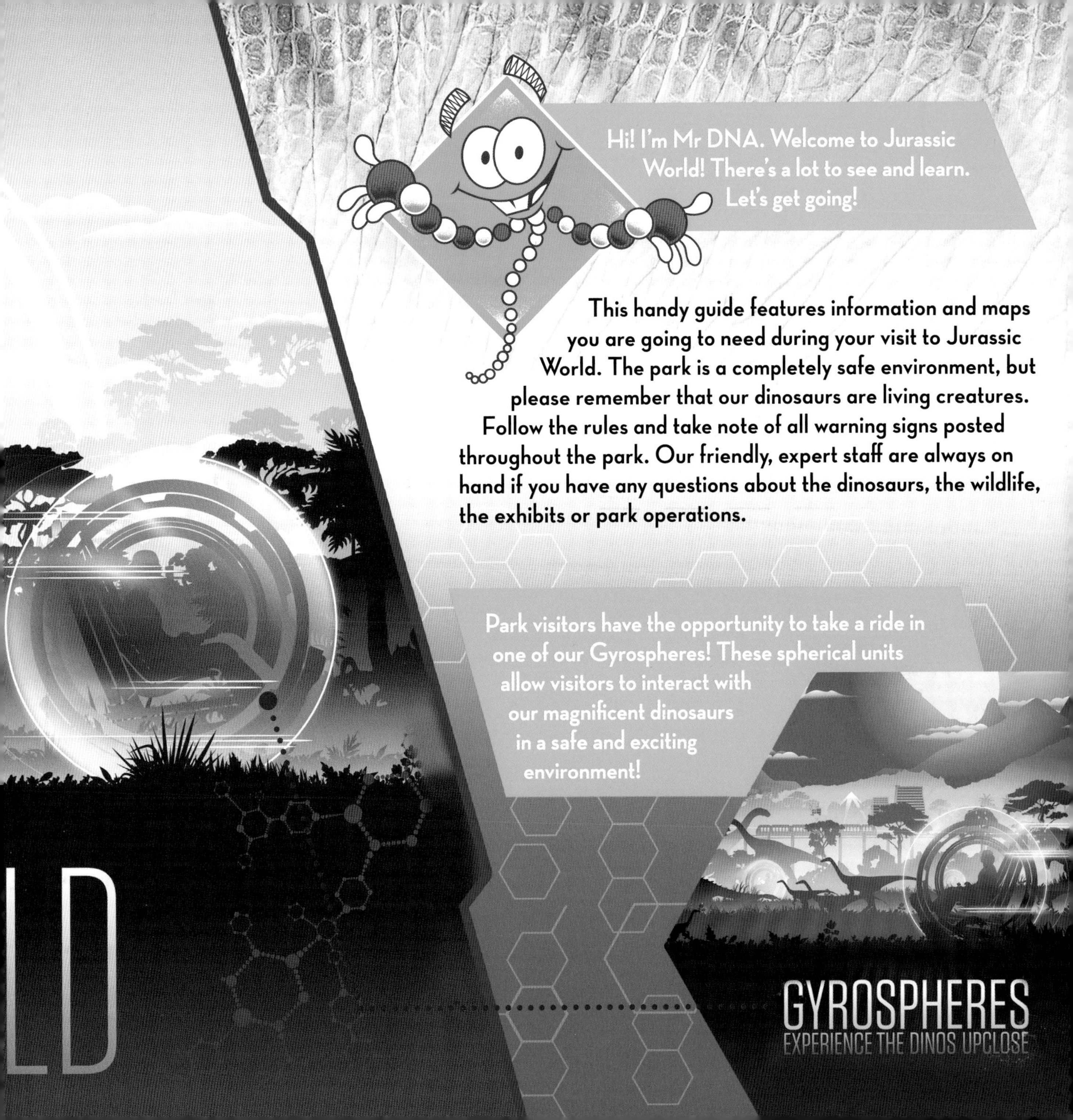

Hi! I'm Mr DNA. Welcome to Jurassic World! There's a lot to see and learn. Let's get going!

This handy guide features information and maps you are going to need during your visit to Jurassic World. The park is a completely safe environment, but please remember that our dinosaurs are living creatures. Follow the rules and take note of all warning signs posted throughout the park. Our friendly, expert staff are always on hand if you have any questions about the dinosaurs, the wildlife, the exhibits or park operations.

Park visitors have the opportunity to take a ride in one of our Gyrospheres! These spherical units allow visitors to interact with our magnificent dinosaurs in a safe and exciting environment!

LD

GYROSPHERES

EXPERIENCE THE DINOS UPCLOSE

MAPS & TRAILS

ISLA NUBLAR

MONORAIL STATION

PARK HIGHLIGHTS

TRICERATOPS TERRITORY

T-REX KINGDOM

MOSASAURUS FEEDING SHOW

GALLIMIMUS VALLEY

CRETACEOUS CRUISE

PACHY ARENA

INNOVATION CENTER

CREATION LAB

UNDERWATER OBSERVATORY

THE AVIARY

THE EGG SPINNER

BAMBOO FOREST

GYROSPHERE

GOLF COURSE

BOTANICAL GARDENS

GENTLE GIANTS PETTING ZOO

WATER PARK

GONDOLA LIFT

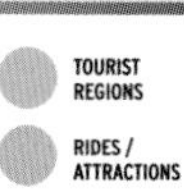

TOURIST REGIONS

RIDES / ATTRACTIONS

DINO SHOWS

SCANNER KIOSKS

MONORAIL STATION

FERRY LANDING

HOTEL COMPLEX

DINING

INFORMATION

CHILD CARE

CALL CENTER

RESTROOM

MEDICAL

RECYCLING

PARK KEY

Jurassic World is home to some of the most amazing dinosaurs and prehistoric creatures that have ever existed! Be on the look out for the dinosaurs featured in this welcome packet, as well as the other amazing animals and wildlife living in the park.

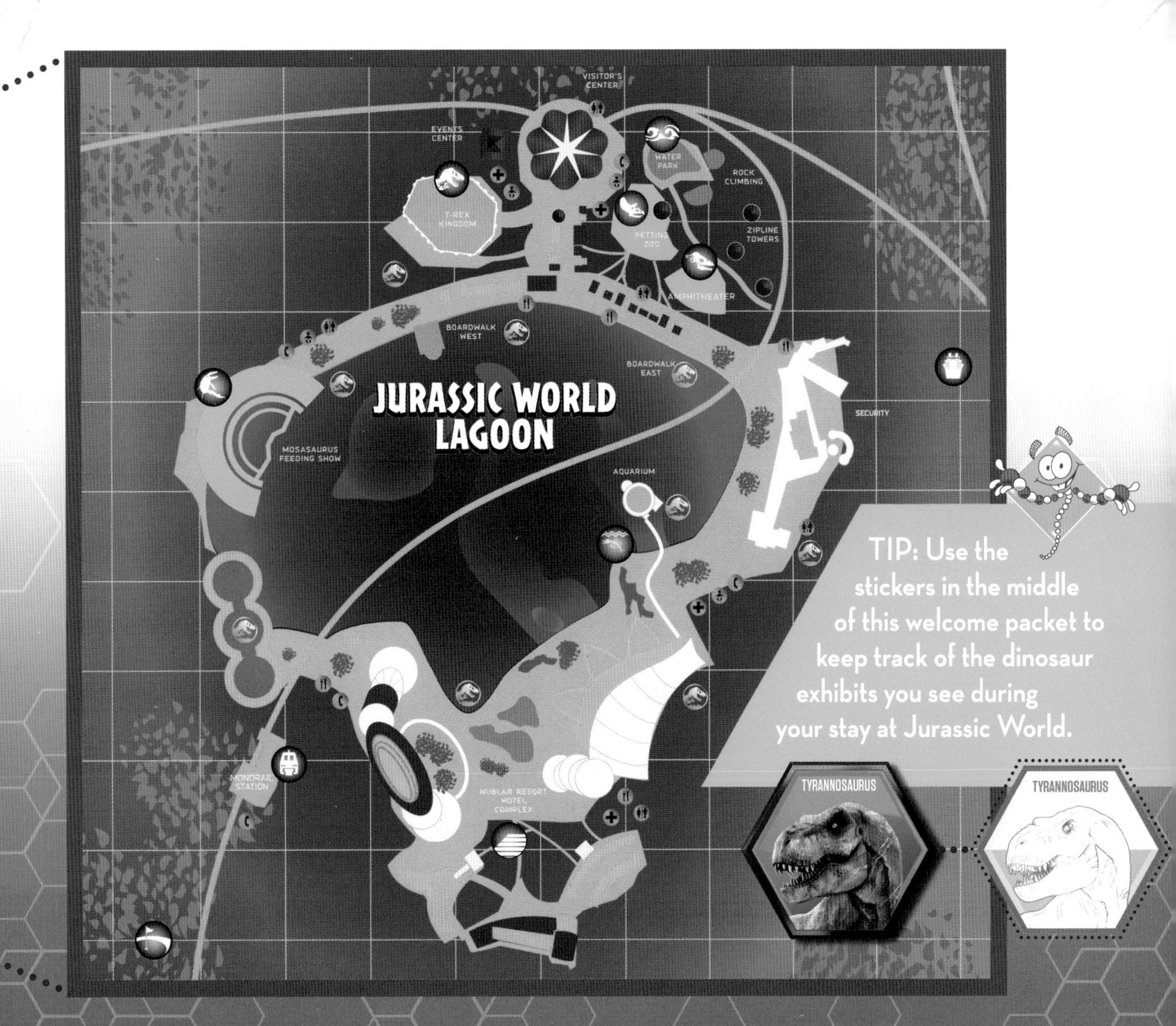

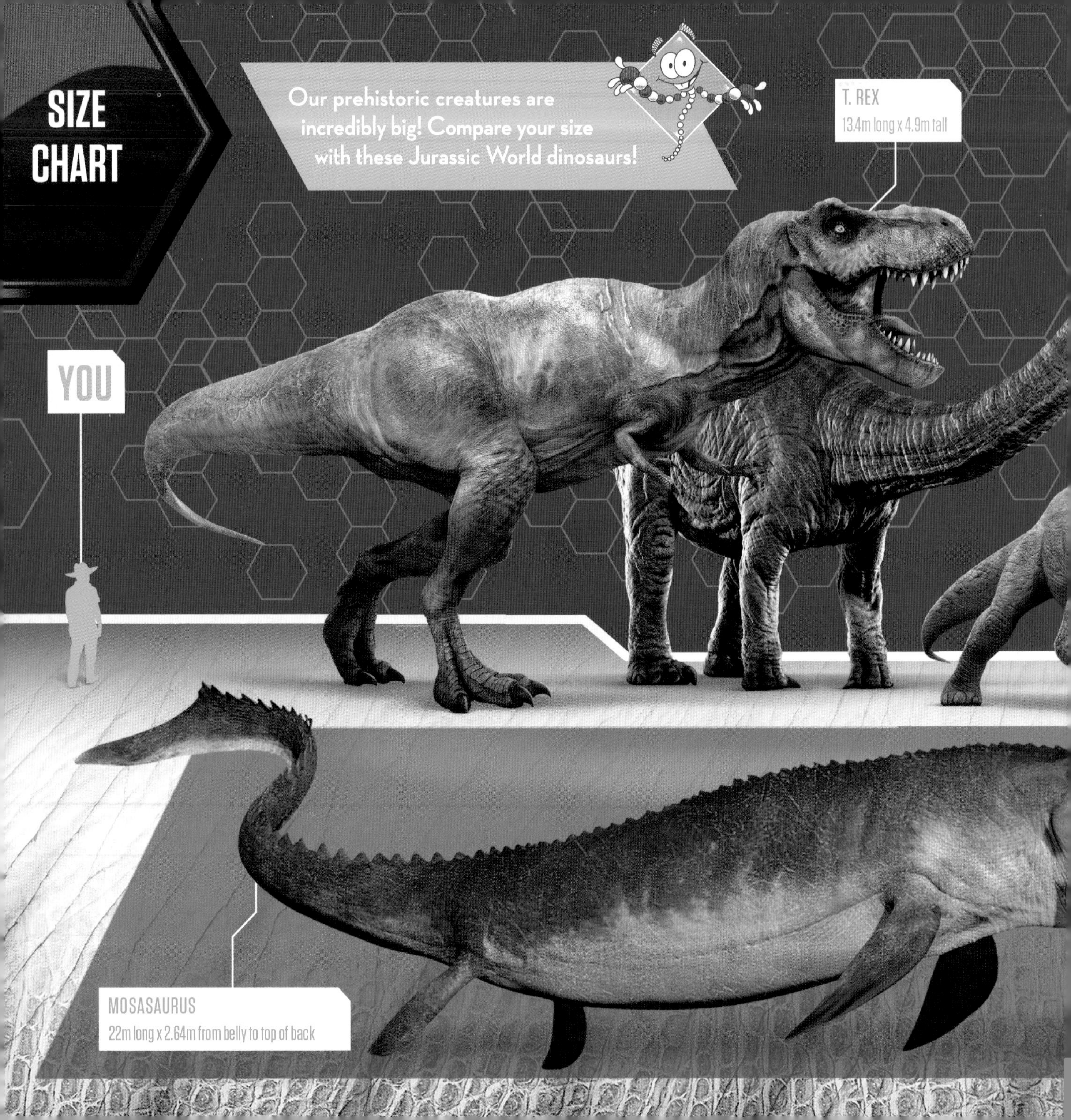
SIZE CHART
Our prehistoric creatures are incredibly big! Compare your size with these Jurassic World dinosaurs!
T. REX
13.4m long x 4.9m tall
YOU
MOSASAURUS
22m long x 2.64m from belly to top of back

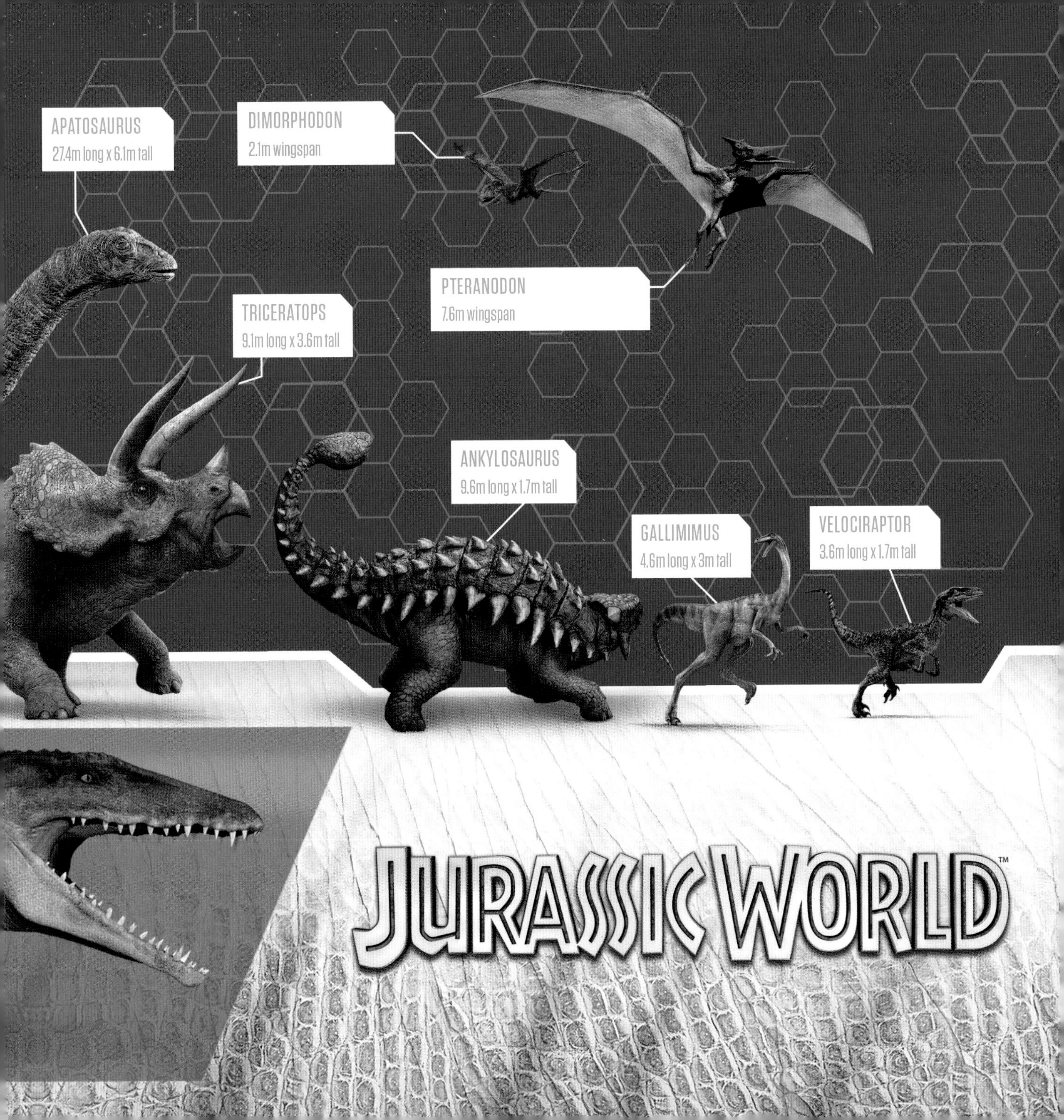

APATOSAURUS
27.4m long x 6.1m tall

DIMORPHODON
2.1m wingspan

PTERANODON
7.6m wingspan

TRICERATOPS
9.1m long x 3.6m tall

ANKYLOSAURUS
9.6m long x 1.7m tall

GALLIMIMUS
4.6m long x 3m tall

VELOCIRAPTOR
3.6m long x 1.7m tall

JURASSIC WORLD™

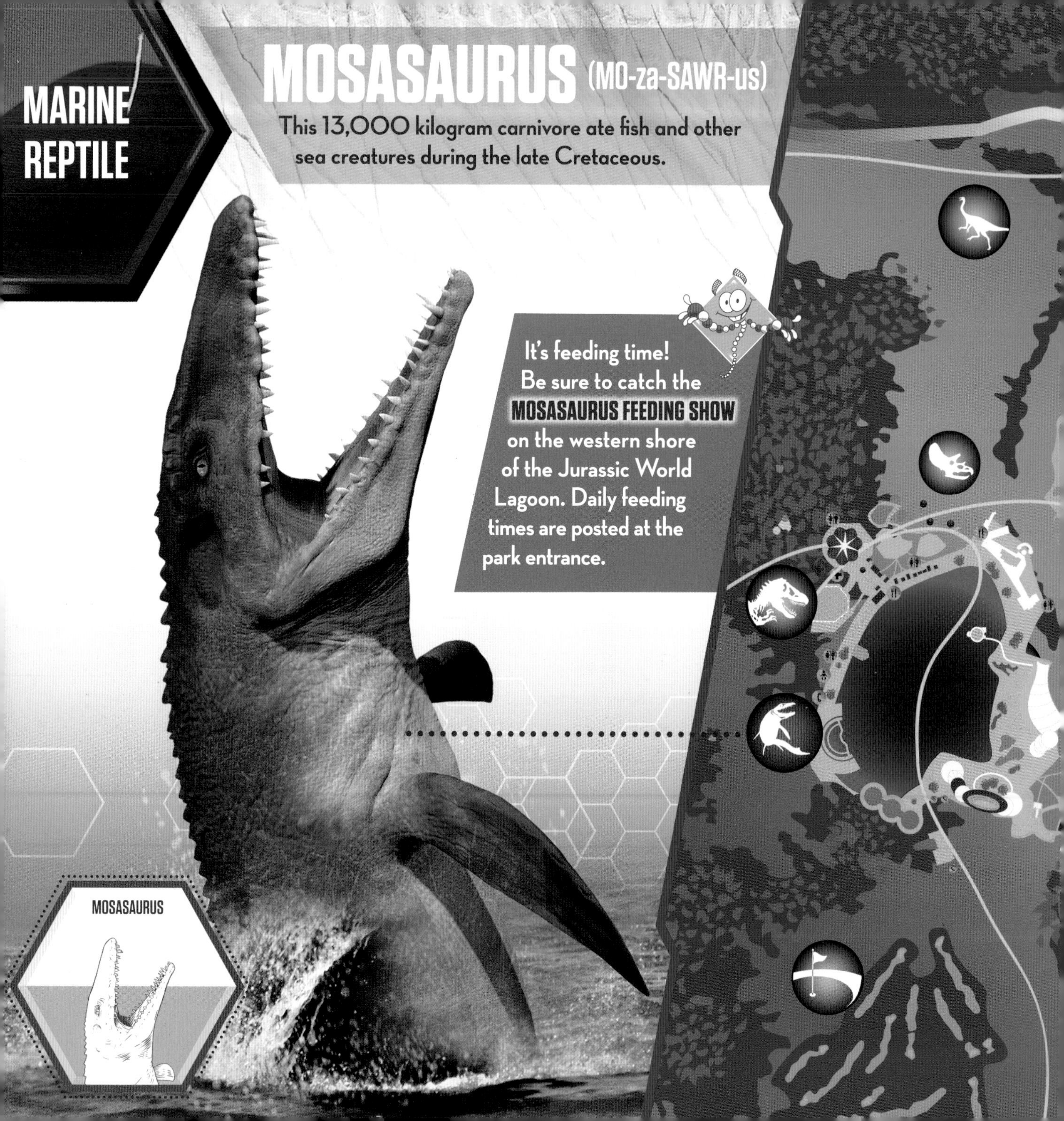
MARINE REPTILE
MOSASAURUS (MO-za-SAWR-us)
This 13,000 kilogram carnivore ate fish and other sea creatures during the late Cretaceous.
It's feeding time! Be sure to catch the MOSASAURUS FEEDING SHOW on the western shore of the Jurassic World Lagoon. Daily feeding times are posted at the park entrance.
MOSASAURUS

FUN FACT: Some scientists believe that the Velociraptor was one of the smartest dinosaur species!

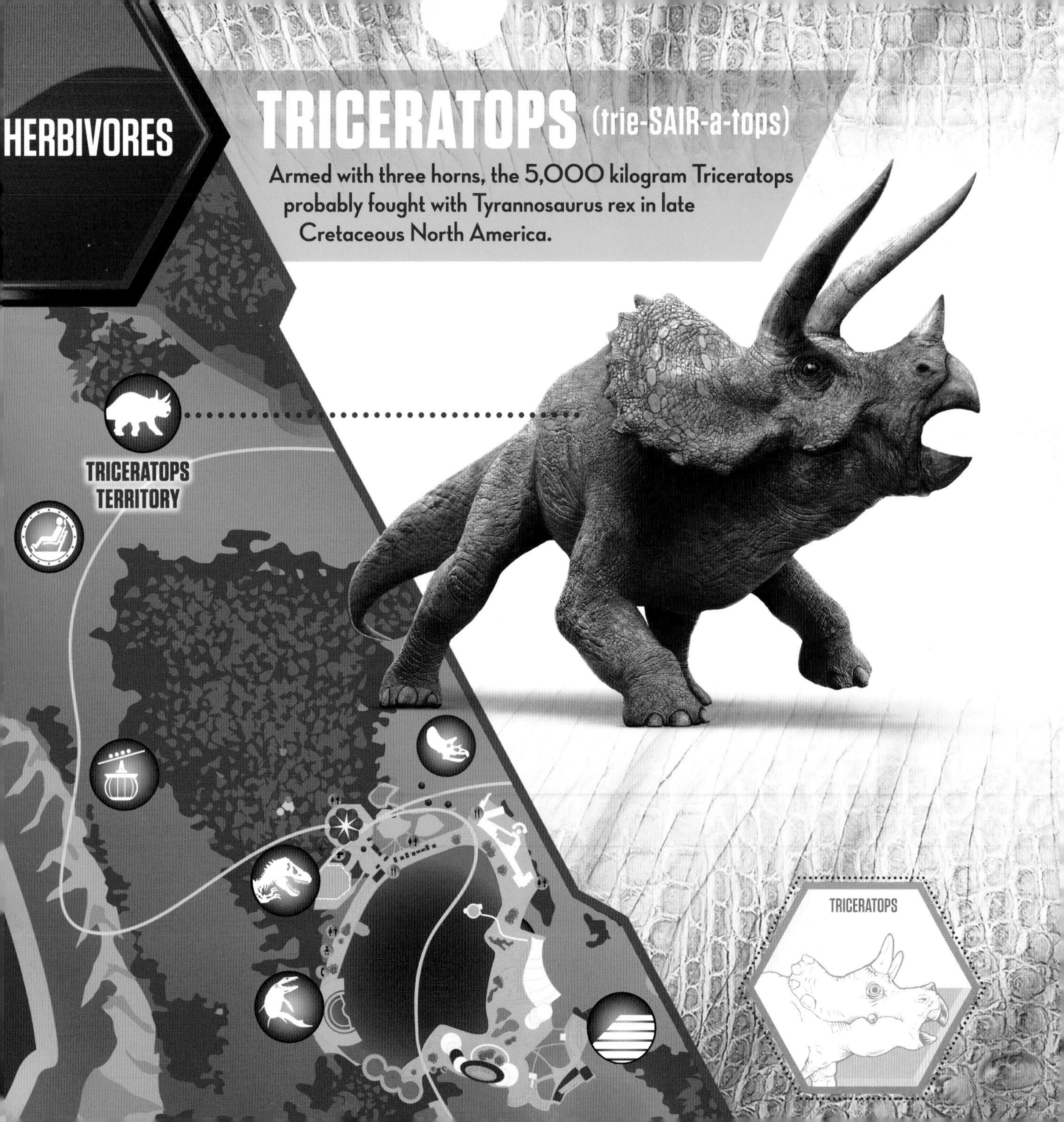
HERBIVORES
TRICERATOPS (trie-SAIR-a-tops)
Armed with three horns, the 5,000 kilogram Triceratops probably fought with Tyrannosaurus rex in late Cretaceous North America.
TRICERATOPS TERRITORY
TRICERATOPS

PACK HUNTERS

VELOCIRAPTOR (vuh-LOS-ih-RAP-tor)

Velociraptors are small, fierce pack hunters. Approximately 3 and a half metres long and weighing 45 kilograms, they work together to bring down prey bigger than themselves.

PTERANODON (te-RAN-o-don)
With its over 7 metre wingspan, this 400 kilogram flying reptile was a master of the late Cretaceous skies over North America.
FLYING REPTILES
THE AVIARY
PTERANODON
DIMORPHODON (die-MOR-fo-don)
Smaller than the Pteranodon, Dimorphodon has a 2 metre wingspan and originally lived 190 million years ago.
DIMORPHODON

ANKYLOSAURUS (ANG-ki-lo-SAWR-us)

Tank-like and low to the ground, this late-Cretaceous dinosaur is covered with armoured plates and spikes. It also has a heavy club at the end of its tail for defence.

Not all of our prehistoric creatures are carnivores, but don't think they are easy prey! In addition to their tremendous size, herbivores had great natural defences such as horns and armour.

APATOSAURUS (a-PAT-o-SAWR-us)

This giant sauropod from the late Jurassic period was over 25 metres and weighed over 15,500 kilograms!

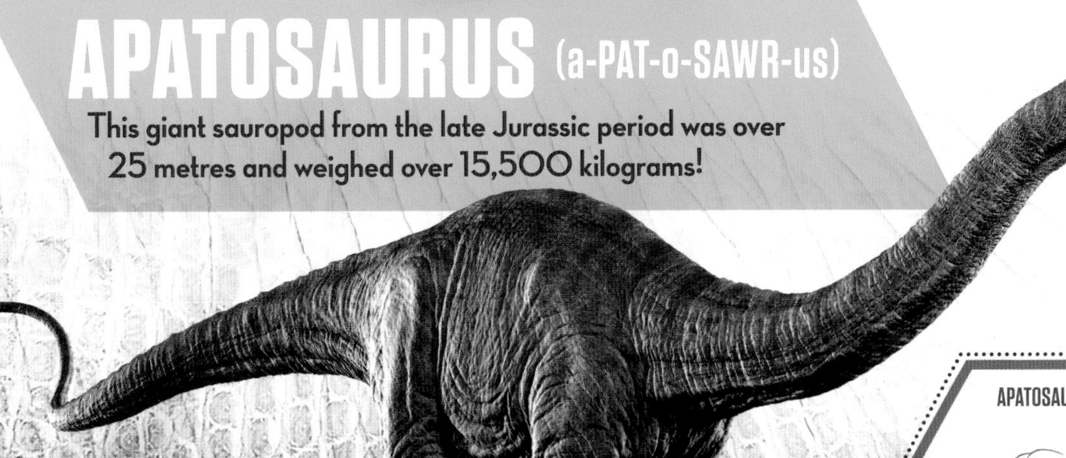

KING OF THE DINOSAURS
TYRANNOSAURUS (tie-RAN-o-SAWR-us)
T. rex was the king of the late Cretaceous period. At 13 metres long and weighing 5,400 kilograms, this carnivore was assumed to be both a hunter and a scavenger.
TYRANNOSAURUS

T.REX
TERRITORY
WARNING
DANGEROUS
TYRANNOSAURUS REX
(TYRANT LIZARD KING)
JURASSIC WORLD
FUN FACT: T. rex probably fought other dinosaurs in the wild, but we never allow our magnificent dinosaurs to harm each other in Jurassic World!

We hope you enjoyed your visit to Jurassic World! Please come back and visit us soon!

FUN FACT: The scientists at the Creation Lab are always hard at work, so you never know what new dinosaurs will be on display next!